TRINITY
COLLEGE LONDON PRESS

Piano
Stories

Motivation, support and inspiration
for creative exam preparation

Grade 1
Trinity College London
Piano Syllabus 2018-2020

Published by
Trinity College London Press Ltd
trinitycollege.com

Registered in England
Company no. 09726123

Author: Nithicha Sivayathorn
Illustrator: Methanan Sivayathorn
Cover illustration: Daofujiki

First impression, February 2018

Printed in England by Caligraving Ltd

About Piano Stories

Piano Stories is a collection of musical activities to be used by teachers and students preparing pieces for Trinity College London Piano syllabus Grade 1 (2018-2020). Through stories, illustrations and explorative exercises, the activities aim to spark music imagination, engage students' interest and aid the learning of pieces in a holistic way.

The ideas are not exhaustive and teachers are highly encouraged to build on these activities to help students discover a wider world of sounds on the keyboard and nurture their sense of achievement and ownership of the music.

Table of Contents

Grade 1

MANGO WALK

JAMAICA

Mango Walk is based on a folk tune from Jamaica, a tropical island in the Caribbean Sea.

Music from the Caribbean often has lively rhythms and uses a lot of syncopation, or notes that fall on unaccented beats.

'Mango Rhythm' is an example of a syncopated rhythm. Notice how some notes fall on the 'and' between the main beats.

Count and clap this rhythm until you think you've got the feel of it.

MANGO RHYTHM

| 1 | + | 2 | + | 3 | + | 4 | + |

Before you play, warm up with these basic dance steps!

GET READY TO DANCE

Make sure to change fingers.

SPINNING AND TURNING

SIDE STEP

Keep the LH pulse steady to help you get the rhythm right.

CARIBBEAN TIME

Let's make up our own Caribbean tune! Play the piece a few times with your teacher. Join in at bar 5. For each bar, pick one note and play it using the 'Mango rhythm' on the opposite page.

For bars that are orange, pick one of these notes.

For bars that are green, pick one of these notes.

Once you have found a tune you like, write it down. You might need to use the 8va sign.

THE MANGO TREE

Colour the mangoes according to their note value.

Allemande

What is an allemande?

An allemande is a dance in $\frac{4}{4}$ from the Renaissance and Baroque period. In those times, dancers kept their backs straight and used small steps and hops.

Look! The dancers take turns to dance to a musical phrase, one couple at a time.

Copy the pattern of the first phrase, but start on G instead.

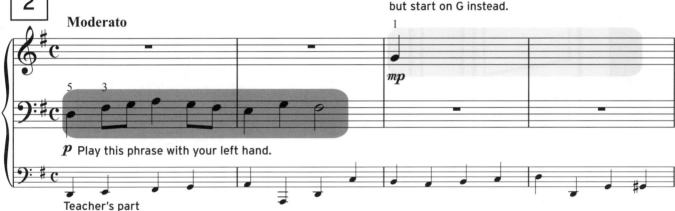

Now start on A. Remember to use C♯ instead of C.

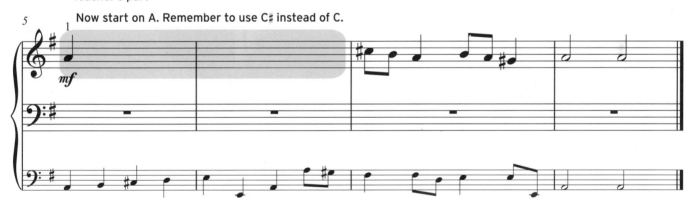

Can you find the starting notes on the keyboard? Colour them using pink, blue, and green!

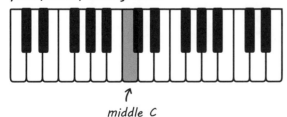

middle C

Notice how the second phrase copies the pattern of the first phrase. This is called imitation.

The third phrase copies the second phrase, but goes up by one note. This is called a sequence.

There are three sequences in 'Allemande'. Can you find them?

Practice these steps carefully! Make sure that your movements are controlled and graceful.

Hop, land and then hop, land!

Clever footwork.

Minuet

Miss Anne and Emily Linfield have been invited to a ball!
The two sisters are very excited to see their sister, Catherine,
who recently married Mr Weston.

The Newlyweds

Mr and Mrs Weston finally arrive.
How happy they are together!

Mrs Weston dances beautifully.

Mr Weston also looks very dashing.

Miss Emily is trying to learn the dance steps.

Now how does that go?   Ah! That's it!

Seeing how happy Mrs Weston looks, Miss Anne and Miss Emily wonder about love. Their hearts flutter a little when they think about falling in love.

When you see a pattern like this, put a slight emphasis on the notes on the main beats (in pink). Play the notes between the main beats softer.

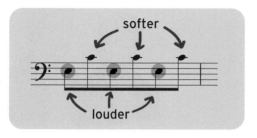

Use a slight rocking motion from your wrist.

Thoughts of Love

Make sure that the whole piece is played very gently without unnecessary accents on your thumb.

Use a coloured pencil to highlight the notes on the main beats in bars 5-8 and 13-15.

Mr Weston comes over.

Anne, Emily, may I introduce you to my cousins
Mr George Egerton and Mr William Hughes.

'Oh, what fine gentlemen!', the two ladies thought.

Minuet

A minuet is a dance in triple time, characterised by small graceful steps.

The minuet dance is choreographed with **six beats** per phrase, which means that each phrase consists of two bars of music. When playing a minuet it is important to remember this and not cut the phrases short. Here is a section of a famous minuet by J S Bach. Listen to your teacher play and write down the phrasing.

Look at your copy of 'Minuet' (*Trinity Piano Exam Pieces Grade 1*, page 5). Can you figure out the phrasing?

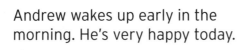

I'm Happy

Andrew wakes up early in the morning. He's very happy today.

I'm happy.

Even the birds outside are happy.

Make sure that the second note is short and 'lifts off' gently.

I'm happy,

Listen to the birds as he slowly hops down the stairs.

As happy as can be.

'Muffin is happy to see me!'

Catch him in your arms!

Make sure that you release your left-hand thumb before your right-hand thumb.

'I wonder if anyone remembers what day this is...'

LEGATO

Legato notes are played smoothly.

STACCATO

Staccato notes are short and not connected.

Imagine the left hand as the sound of your heart beating in anticipation, while the right hand sings in long phrases of hope! Follow along as your teacher plays it for you first.

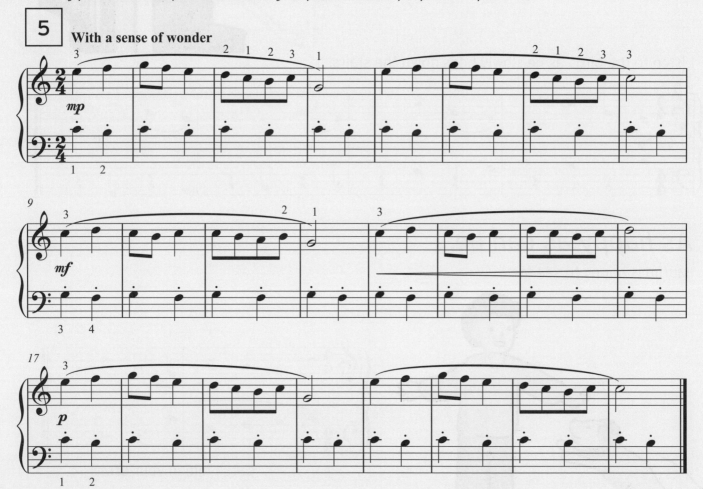

15

'Everyone remembers it is my birthday!'

I'm happy.

I'm happy.

Come celebrate with me!

Take a deep breath.

And blow out the candles!

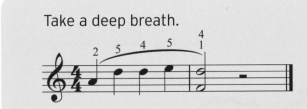 

Write *mp* and a crescendo under both phrases!

Look at all the presents, let's see what's in the biggest box.

I'm happy.

I'm happy.

My heart is full of joy.

Fiddle with the knot...

Pull the ribbon...

Lift the lid...

Write *mf* under all three phrases!

Content:

Here:

'It's a toy triceratops! Exactly what I've always wanted!'

Try to hold your thumb down!

I'm happy.

I'm happy.   *I've got a brand new toy!*

Press the button on the triceratops' tail to hear him roar! What does he sound like?

You can even make up your own: try using some black keys or note clusters for some dinosaur-like sounds! Remember to add some dynamics.

I'm happy.

I'm happy.

Come meet my brand new toy!

The words in orange text on pages 43–46 are lyrics that will fit with the piece 'I'm Happy' (*Trinity Piano Exam Pieces Grade 1*, page 6)

Look at the music and see if you can sing along!

Just for Starters

There is food on the table in the dining room. The family has not come down to dinner yet. The door is left ajar.

Do you hear the tiptoes? Guess who is coming?

It's little people who are secretly living in the house! They often come out when no-one is looking! Today they have crept out to find the food left on the dining table.

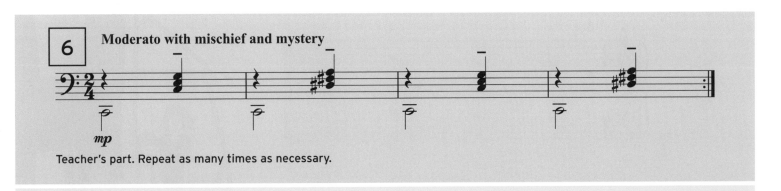

6 Moderato with mischief and mystery

mp

Teacher's part. Repeat as many times as necessary.

Student's part.

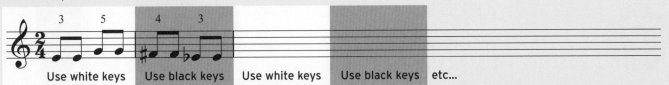

Use white keys   Use black keys   Use white keys   Use black keys   etc...

Remember to play with your fingertips for a real tiptoe sound!

Listen as your teacher plays the accompaniment. Then join in with your own 'tiptoeing' sound. Start in the five-finger position with the thumb on middle C and alternate between playing one bar on white keys and one bar on black keys.

If you feel more adventurous you can change hand positions and use any notes!

Let's Get to Work!

The family of little people is trying to get up onto the table, which is very high!

First they must throw up the hook!

Not quite there yet!   Yes!

Then, to get up, they make their own lift...
Up, up, up we go!

Do you know which interval the right hand plays?

It is a ....

Can you find a few more of these intervals on the keyboard?

What about the interval in the left hand?

It is a ....

Can you find a few more of these intervals on the keyboard?

Suddenly a cat appears! Oh no!

Sometimes you need to play a black key with your little finger.
Make sure that you use the black key position for these situations (see below).

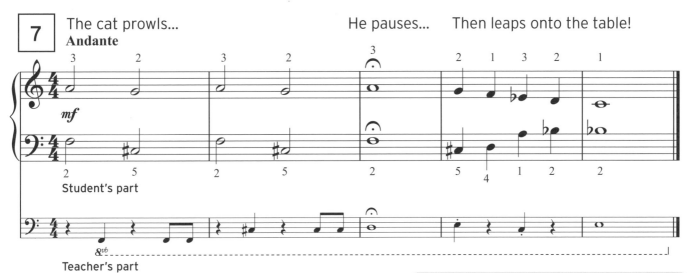

7 The cat prowls...   He pauses...   Then leaps onto the table!
Andante

Student's part

Teacher's part

Suddenly the little people have a bright idea.

They take a crouton and throw it onto the floor to distract the cat.

Black key position

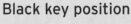

When you have to play a lot of black keys, moving your hand further up into the keyboard can make it easier to play.

Lift...   and throw...

Aim well and make sure that the crouton lands right in front of the cat!

Where is the Cat?

As the little people make their way home with their food, they need to look out for the cat. Listen as your teacher plays these short tunes and write down the correct dynamic markings.

If the melody is played softly, the cat is far away: write *p*

If the melody is played loudly, the cat is near: write *f*

Getting Home

Are the little people walking normally or are they on tiptoes?

Listen as your teacher plays the following melodies and decide whether they are staccato (tiptoes) or legato (walking normally). Write staccato dots under the notes which sound detached.

Bonus point: make up a few short melodies and play them on the keyboard and have your teacher guess if the little people are on tiptoes or walking normally.

The Enchanted Garden

Hidden behind a secret gate,
An enchanted garden lies,
Where pixies play and fairies roam,
Where golden unicorns call their home,
Where imps and elves and nymphs and gnomes
Make merry beneath the skies.

Use your left hand to play this figure. You will notice that the note 'A' has its stem pointing down, while the other notes have their stems pointing up. This means that there are two parts, or voices, sounding at the same time.

Don't let go of the A!

Hold the A down with your 4th finger.

An Enchanted Afternoon in the Garden

Take a stroll in the enchanted garden.
Imagine all the beautiful things we'll see!

10 Teacher's part (RH)
Secretly brimming with magic!

mp

Student's part (LH)

6

11

✎ Make the enchanted garden more interesting by adding these musical symbols however you like!

a tempo

rit.

Can you think of a few more musical symbols?
Ask your teacher for some more ideas.

Fairies of the Garden

Make the enchanted garden more interesting by adding
these musical symbols however you like!

11 ## Purple Dahlia

*Purple Dahlia is delighted to meet you,
Her colourful petals open to greet you!*

Student's part (LH)

Play softly with your thumb and lift off at the end of each phrase.

12 ## Cherry Blossom

*Cherry Blossom, pink and fair,
Her gentle fragrance fills the air!*

Student's part (LH)

Remember to play the chords with arm weight and aim for a nice deep sound.

Red Berry

*Always moving, always merry,
Meet the fun-loving little Red Berry!*

13 Student's part (RH)

Magical Flight

Join the twin fairies on their magical flight around the garden.

Colour all the fifths yellow

Colour all the fourths orange

Colour all the thirds using a colour of your choice

Walking and Talking

The sun is out and the big city is buzzing with life and activity. Let's take a walk and see what everyone is doing.

Rhythm help

You can use the words in the speech balloons as rhythmic cues to help you count.

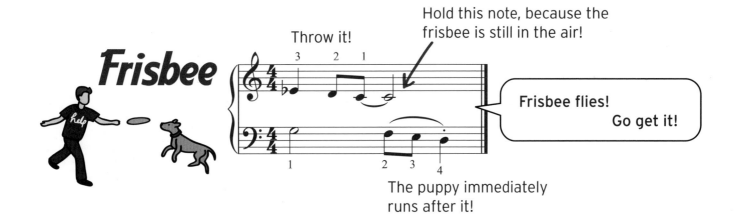

Frisbee

Throw it!

Hold this note, because the frisbee is still in the air!

Frisbee flies!
Go get it!

The puppy immediately runs after it!

Rooftop Dancers

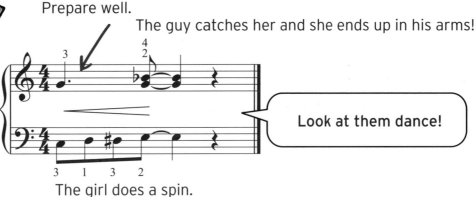

Prepare well.

The guy catches her and she ends up in his arms!

Look at them dance!

The girl does a spin.

Cyclist Couple

Over the speed bumps together.

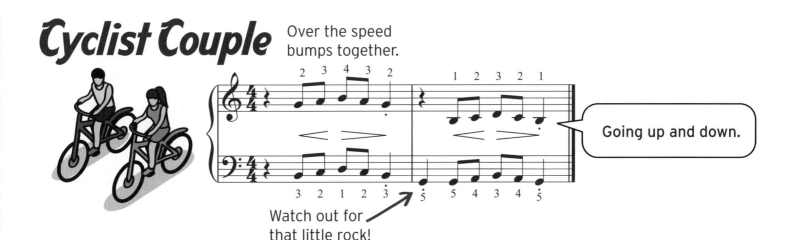

Going up and down.

Watch out for that little rock!

In the past, shepherds in the Alps used a special kind of singing to communicate across long distances and over valleys.

This later becomes known as a form of music called yodeling (jodeling), which uses a lot of rapid changes between low voice and high voice.

Did you know?

The word yodel is derived from the German word jodeln, meaning 'to utter the syllable "jo" ' (pronounced 'yo').

Joseph grew up in a rural village in the Alps. When he was a boy he used to hear shepherds yodeling across the mountains. It always made him feel happy and at peace.

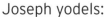
Joseph yodels:

And listens to the yodel echoing back from the valleys.

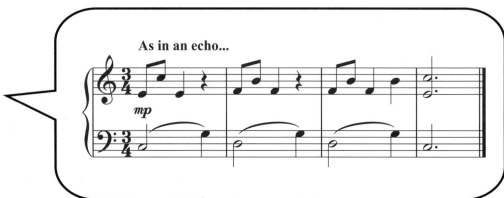

Let's Yodel

Create your own yodelling part by using just your index fingers.
Play four quavers in each bar, alternating between your left and right hands.
Use the suggested notes below.

For bars highlighted in yellow, use keys highlighted in yellow.

For bars highlighted in pink, use keys highlighted in pink.

 On the keyboard diagrams above, write down the names of the highlighted notes and figure out the chords that they form.

Stick thin strips of sticky notes onto the keyboard to make it easier to see which notes to use.

Listen as your teacher plays the first eight bars of this piece, then it's your turn to start yodeling!

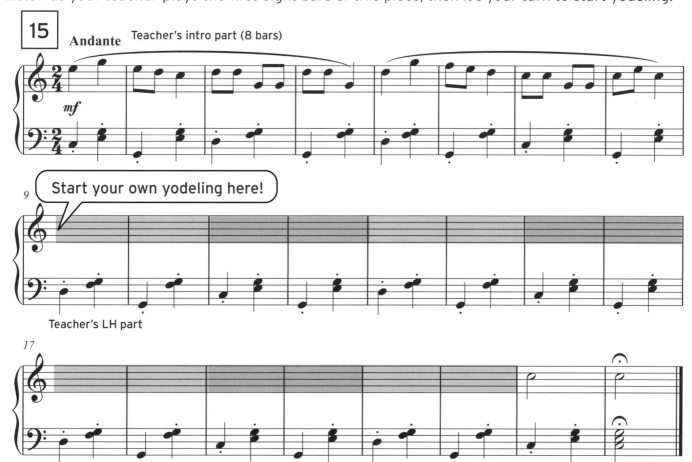

30

As Joseph grew up, he heard people say that life in a city was better. So one day he packed his bags and took the train to the nearest city.

There were many things to do and see in the big city.
He rode the horse-drawn tram for the first time!

16 **Grandly!**

mf

Student's part (LH)

He finally found work in a leather factory. This is what the machine sounds like!

Busily!

Knock or tap on the piano lid with your left hand.

But life in a factory was not as Joseph had expected. It was often very hard work, with all the workers crammed together in a small room.

Working hard! **17**

Student's part (RH)

mf

Teacher's part (LH)

Brace yourself for some heavy lifting!

f

Nostalgic Reverie

Soon Joseph started to feel that the busy city was full of stress, and he missed his peaceful village in the Alps.

Late one night, he climbed up to the roof of his lodging and gazed at the mountain range on the horizon. With the moon shining bright above him, he started yodeling.

And it seemed that from afar, across the city deep in slumber, he heard yodeling sweetly echoing back.

FINISH

Hand in Hand

Benjamin the otter is out one day swimming along the coast, when he spots something in the sand on the beach.

It is a pair of trendy sunglasses! He quickly puts them on and looks around.

Amazingly, everything now seems to be much cooler than before!

Even Mr Crab suddenly looks cool as he chills out by himself.

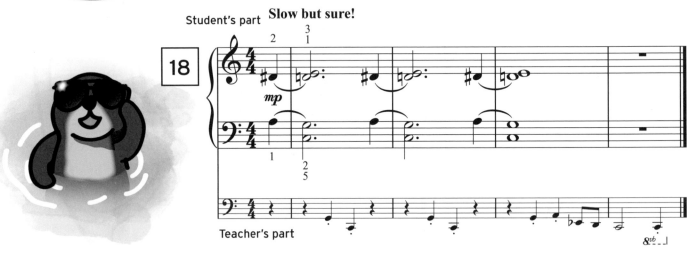

He taps a cool rhythm with seashells.

Suddenly he realises that someone has been watching him. It's another otter, Josephine. She thinks his rhythm sounds very nice.

Chillin' in the Blues

Benjamin and Josephine like each other a lot and decide to spend a lazy afternoon floating around together in the blue sea.

Listen as your teacher plays this piece and join in with your own melody in bars 9-16 using the 'seashell rhythm', choosing from any of the notes highligted in yellow below, and ending every phrase with a G.

Example student's part:

20 Lazily

5

9 Join in the fun!

13

If you need more time to experiment, you can agree with your teacher to repeat bars 9-16 as many times as you like!

17

As they are floating along, suddenly they hear very lively music from a cruise ship.

It's a rock and roll band in full swing!

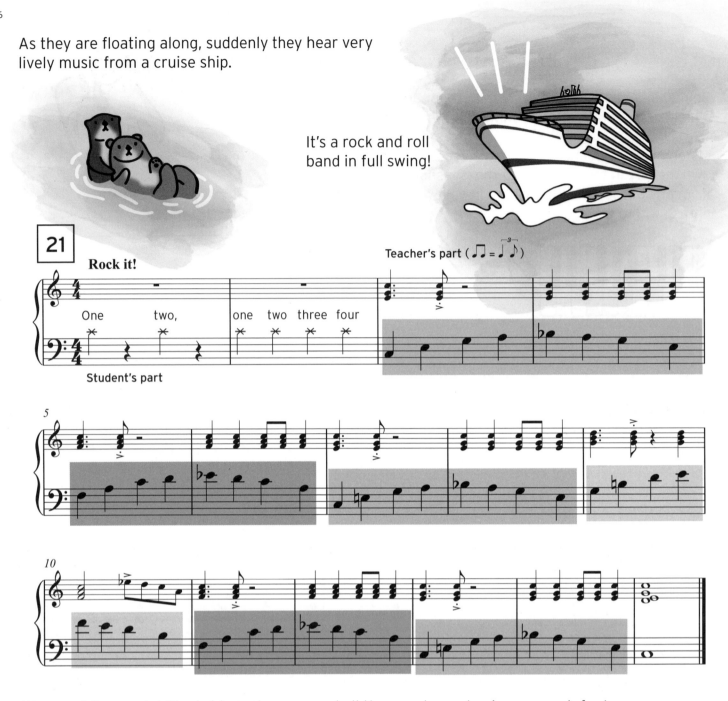

It's a wedding party! The bride and groom and all the guests are having so much fun!

Benjamin suddenly has a very happy thought as he looks at Josephine.